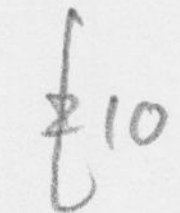

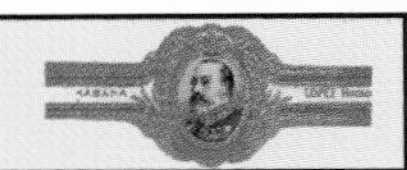

# CUBAN TOBACCO

**WHY CUBAN CIGARS ARE THE WORLD'S BEST.**

by Eumelio Espino Marrero

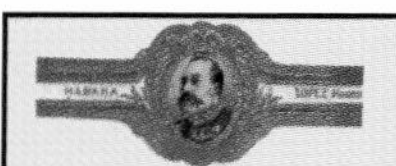

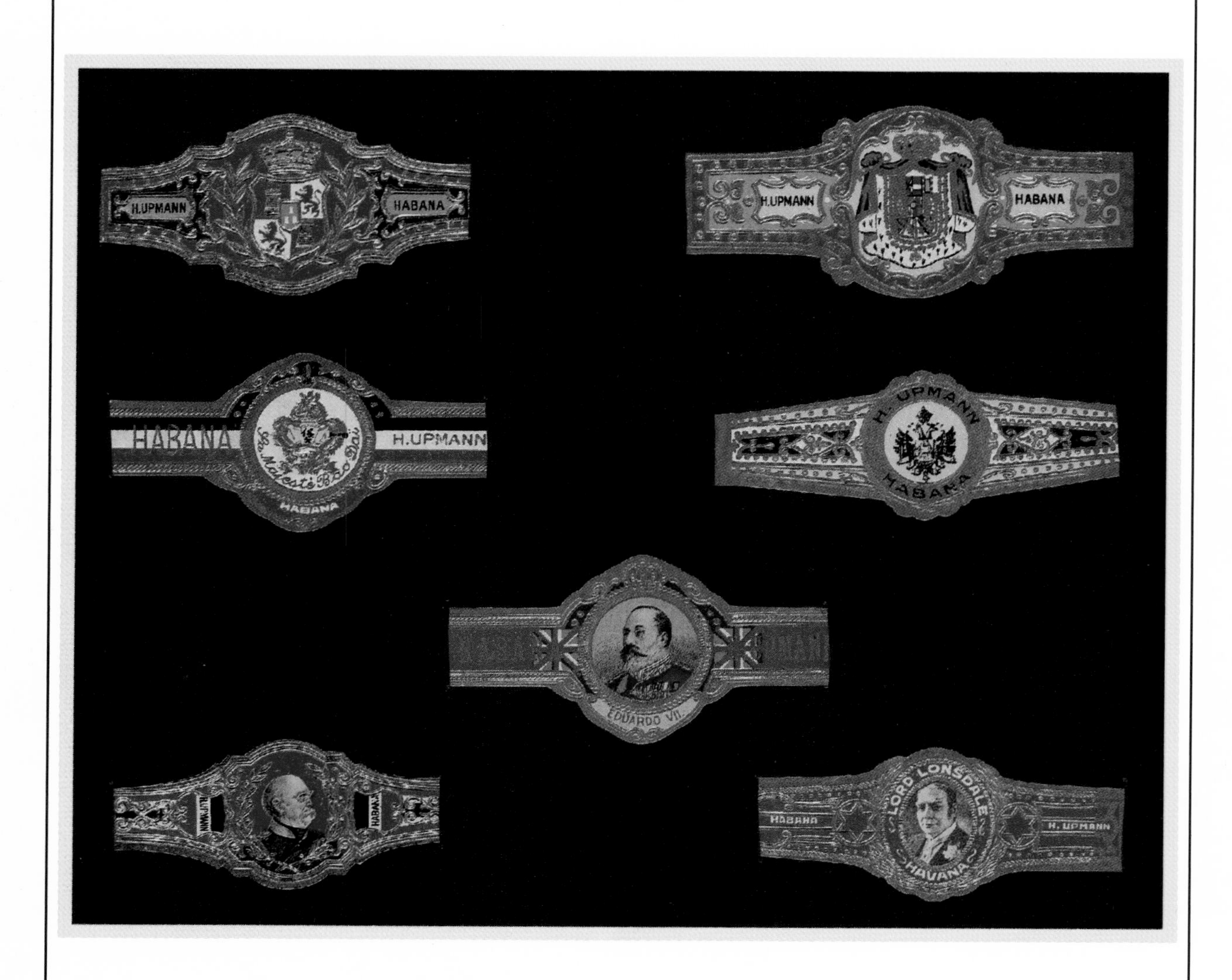

Distributed in the UNITED STATES to the Pet Trade by T.F.H. Publications, Inc., One T.F.H. Plaza, Neptune City, NJ 07753; distributed in the UNITED STATES to the Bookstore and Library Trade by National Book Network, Inc. 4720 Boston Way, Lanham MD 20706; in CANADA to the Pet Trade by H & L Pet Supplies Inc., 27 Kingston Crescent, Kitchener, Ontario N2B 2T6; Rolf C. Hagen Inc., 3225 Sartelon St. Laurent-Montreal Quebec H4R 1E8; in CANADA to the Book Trade by Vanwell Publishing Ltd., 1 Northrup Crescent, St. Catharines, Ontario L2M 6P5 ; in ENGLAND by T.F.H. Publications, PO Box 15, Waterlooville PO7 6BQ; in AUSTRALIA AND THE SOUTH PACIFIC by T.F.H. (Australia), Pty. Ltd., Box 149, Brookvale 2100 N.S.W., Australia; in NEW ZEALAND by Brooklands Aquarium Ltd. 5 McGiven Drive, New Plymouth, RD1 New Zealand; in Japan by T.F.H. Publications, Japan—Jiro Tsuda, 10-12-3 Ohjidai, Sakura, Chiba 285, Japan; in SOUTH AFRICA by Lopis (Pty) Ltd., P.O. Box 39127, Booysens, 2016, Johannesburg, South Africa. Published by T.F.H. Publications, Inc.

MANUFACTURED IN THE
UNITED STATES OF AMERICA
BY T.F.H. PUBLICATIONS, INC.

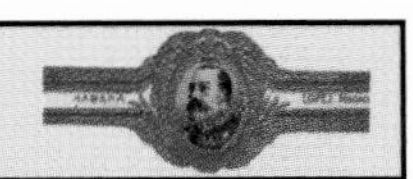

# CONTENTS

ESPECIALES HABANA
ESPECIALES HABANA
ESPECIALES GAMBUS HABANA
ESPECIALES GAMBUS HABANA
RFG. Co.
HABANA
HABANA
Berwind
REPUBLICA DE CUBA
PRESIDENCIA
HABANA
JOSÉ MORALES Y CA.
EXCEPCIONALES
BH
HABANA
BOLIVAR
HABANA
BELINDA
MITTERSILL CLUB
LA GLORIA CUBANA
HABANA
HABANA
EL VICTORIOSO
MADE IN HAVANA CUBA

# ORIGINS OF ITS CULTIVATION IN CUBA

The species *Nicotiana tabacum* L. is a natural amphidiploid between the *Nicotiana sylvestris* and one of the species of the tomentosae section. According to the detailed investigations by Gerstel (1960) and other researchers, it is reasonable to assume that the species is the *Nicotiana tomentosiformis* Goodspeed.

From the phytogeographic data on the dispersion of the *N.tabacum* predecesors (*N. sylvestris* and *N. tomentosiformis*) it follows that the genetic origin of the *N. tabacum*, as an interspecific primary hybrid, can be placed in the area comprised by the pre-mountainous region of the Andes in present day Bolivia, the exact intersection of the areas where the *N. sylvestris* and *N. tomentosiformis* are found.

**On November 2, 1492 Christopher Columbus and his men are presented with dried tobacco leaves by the Cuban indians. This historic moment was captured in many old illustrations like this one.**

Taking the term "center of origin", coined by Vavilov (1926), as the meeting place between a species' genetic origin and the center where that species was initially cultivated, the area of the *N. tabacum's* center of origin can be broadened to the Peruvian - Ecuatorian - Bolivian Andes, the seat of the ancient Inca and Chibcha civilizations, whose peoples were the first to grow this species.

Numerous findings indicate that the *N. tabacum* was grown for a long time in the American continent and that the area dedicated to its cultivation covered the territories occupied today by Mexico, Central America, the Caribbean and vast portions of South America. This great dispersion over different climates and types of soils originated a variety of eco-agricultural strains adapted to that very diversity of natural conditions which constitute the direct predecessors of the tobacco varieties known today.

According to Mangelsdorf and Smith (1949), the existing paleontological data place the beginning of maize cultivation in Mexico somewhere between 6000 and 5000 BC, while in Central and South America it can be traced back to 3000 to 2000 BC. It is therefore reasonable to assume that it was precisely during this period of contact that the introduction of tobacco to Central America and Mexico occurred, following a route exactly opposite to that of maize. Consequently, it was during the course of that same period that tobacco also came into the Antilles and Cuba.

During Columbus' first voyage, while his ships were at anchor in the bay known today as Gibara, on 2 November 1492, indigenous Cubans showed the Admiral and his men a few dried leaves of a plant that was totally unknown to the Europeans but seemed to be cherished dearly by the natives. Puzzled by the origin and possible uses of the leaves, Columbus ordered two of his men, Rodrigo de Xerez and Luís de Torres, to take two of the natives as guides and march inland to find out what those leaves so enthusiastically presented to him by the islanders really were. A few days later, the two men came back with the news that the natives used that "grass" in various ways: inhaling the powder of the ground dried leaves, inhaling the smoke produced by burning the leaves mixed with other hallucinatory plants or - what struck them as most impressive - by directly smoking small bunches of those dried leaves rolled into "muskets", a shape that somewhat resembles modern cigars.

Quoting from Brooks, Ortiz (1963) states that the tobacco plants found by the Spaniards in Cuba were *Nicotiana rústica*. Nevertheless, in his treatise "The Nicotiana Gender", Goodspeed (1954) clearly established that at the time of the Conquest, the growing of *N. tabacum* was commonplace throughout Venezuela, Brasil, Perú, Central America and the Antilles, while the *N. rústica* was grown in the present territories of Mexico, the United States and in parts of Canada. The fact that no wild forms of *N.rústica* have ever been found in Cuba - which is not the case in Mexico and the United States - further demonstrates the viewpoint that the species grown by Cuba's early inhabitants were actually strains of *N. tabacum* that had become adapted to the particular conditions of the island.

There are numerous theories as to how tobacco was introduced in Cuba. One of the most widely accepted versions singles out the Arawak Indians, the forefathers of the Cuban Taínos who migrated from the South American mainland into the Antilles, as the bearers of the original seeds and the founders of tobacco cultivation in the Caribbean islands, very specially in Cuba. Rodríguez Ramos (1905), offers the first account of the techniques used for growing, harvesting and treating tobacco. His story is based on the annotations made in 1541 by Demetrio Pela, a Spaniard who for many years grew tobacco together with Cuban natives. Pela's notes indicate that the indigenous population already knew how to sow the seeds, tend the seedplots, transplant the shoots, harvest the leaves, dry and age these in "pilones" (stacks) and

**The Cuban indians at the end of the 1400's used tobacco leaves in many ways. They mixed the tobacco leaves with other leaves and inhaled the smoke.**

**The Cuban indians also rolled the dried tobacco leaves into cigar-shaped bundles and smoked it in a way similar to the way modern man enjoys his cigar.**

wrap them up with "yaguas" (bark sheddings of the royal palm tree), a laborious process quite similar to the one still used today. Such an elaborate standard procedure could only come as a result of long years of experience cultivating the plant, which proves its very early presence on Cuban soil.

Starting in 1520, the Spanish settlers in Cuba began to grow tobacco but only to meet their individual demands of a product to which they had already become attached. Not until the second half of the 16th Century did tobacco attain significance as an internationally prized commodity; for Cuba this marked the beginning of an era of continous expansion of tobacco cultivation for commercial purposes. The first tobacco plantations in the island were sown near the coastal towns and on the banks of the fullest rivers, like the Cauto, in the former province of Oriente, and the Arimao, in the modern province of Cienfuegos. The reason for choosing these particular locations was to facilitate contact with foreign ships and smuggle the produce out of the island, because all trade in tobacco was strictly monopolized at the times by the Spanish Crown. However, by 1719, the growers were turning to the westernmost region of the island, today's Pinar del Río province -then called New Philipines- where they found the best natural conditions for obtaining a product of the highest organoleptic quality.

The first official tobacco plantations were established on the fringe plains of rivers in Cuba.

J.S. MURIAS y Cª
FLOR
FINA
HABANA

LOPEZ HERMANOS & Cº
TAMPA
HABANA
TAMPA – HABANA

# BRIEF HISTORY OF ITS EVOLUTION

After its discovery by the Spaniards, tobacco continued to be grown in Cuba for more than a century in small areas and under the very harsh restrictions imposed by the King of Spain to prevent overproduction of the plant beyond its existing demand as a medicinal herb. Restrictions notwithstanding, the cultivation of tobacco kept growing as did its clandestine trade with the hundreds of sailors who stopped at the various Cuban ports - very especially Havana - around which the tobacco plantations multiplied, turning its suburbs into the main development region of this crop on the island.

By Royal Decree dated October 20, 1614, the free growing of tobacco was finally authorized in Cuba, but its commerce remained forbidden under penalty of death. Only the King could trade in Cuban tobacco. In spite of these regulations, the free sowing of the plant brought about an increase of cultivation and illegal trade, which in time began to be seen as legal. The industry and commercialization of tobacco attained such prominence in Cuba that when the Factory and Monopoly Regime was introduced by Royal Decree of April 11, 1717, the growers in Havana took up arms and rebelled on three succesive ocassions. The last uprising on February 18, 1723, left 13 tobacco farmers dead and many wounded.

The monopoly, which forced the island to sell all its tobacco to the Spanish Crown, simply boosted contraband and smuggling. These procedures were undoubtedly alternate routes of commercialization, but were totally inadequate to promote any meaningful development of the agricultural and industrial potentials of the island. The former continued to be circumscribed to the small plantations that had sprung up near the coastal townships, in spite of the fact that since 1659, the Governor Don Juan Salamanca had authorized the farmers of Trinidad to freely grow tobacco on the plains next to the Agabama, Caracusey and Arimao Rivers. These plains used to be called "vegas", a term that has since identified any

Estas armas de Cifuentes
Que dió el Infante Pelayo
Las pintan con grande ensayo
Según lo saben las gentes.
Y este tal aun con los dientes
Más fuerte que este león
Peleó en su defensión
Con las cruces aparentes.
HABANA
ROMEO Y JULIETA
G. SENSAT
BARCELONA
IBERIA-HABANA
HABANA
HONI SOIT QUI MAL Y PENSE
HABANA
JOSE GENER
HABANA
ROMEO Y JULIETA
HABANA
HABANA
HABANA
LA CORONA
H. DE CABANAS
Y CARVAJAL

tobacco plantation, while "veguero", the plantation man, identifies the tobacco farmer. These "vegas" or plantations on the banks of the aforementioned rivers were the first to be officially legalized in Cuba.

The Royal Decree of March 11, 1798, proclaimed all rivers and their banks to be patrimony of the Crown and authorized the cultivation of tobacco in all the plains crossed by these rivers, whether those lands belonged to the large cattle ranchers or not. This Decree opened great possibilities for the cultivation of tobacco in Cuba and its consequences soon became apparent. Regardless of the absolute control by the monopoly - in place since 1717 - the number of tobacco plantations began to grow and, consequently, the manufacture of cigars, already regarded as the best in the world, increased manifold. This expansion and the steady progress of the industry made it impossible for the monopoly to maintain its constraints much longer. On June 23, 1817, King Ferdinand VII signed a Royal Decree eliminating the priviliges theretofore enjoyed by the Factory and abolishing the obsolete monopoly. The cultivation and commercialization of tobacco at last became a legal activity open for all.

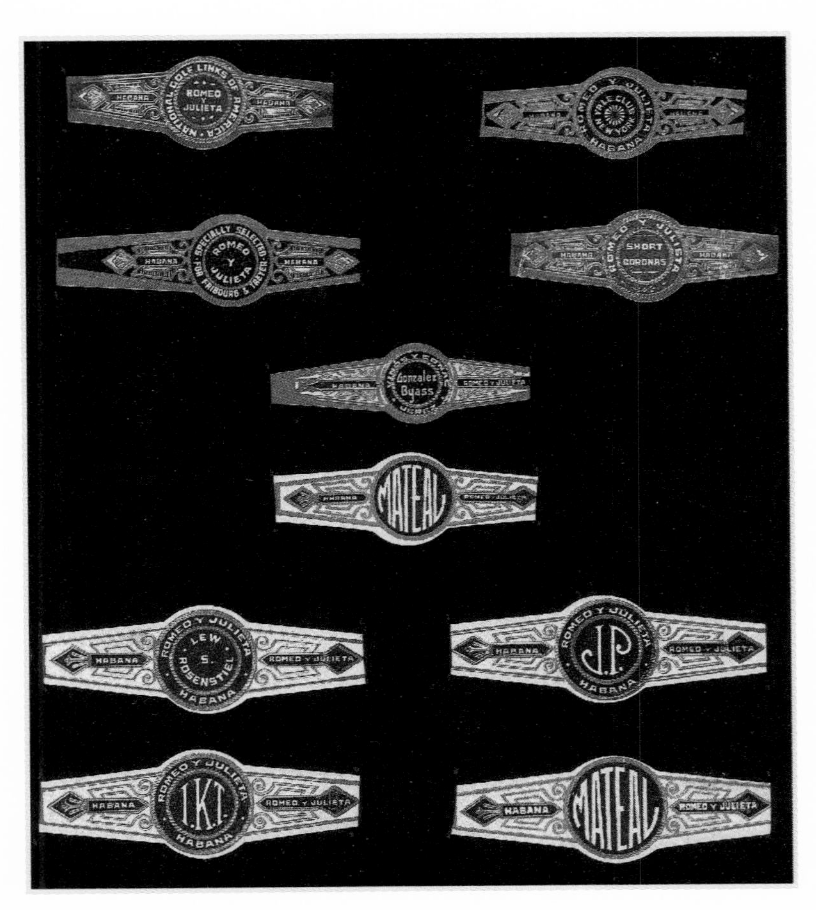


The abolition of the monopoly did not bring an immediate increase in the cultivation of the plant due to the exhorbitant taxes and deductions that the Crown imposed on its production. Suffice it to say that the King had to receive one twentieth of the entire tobacco yield of the island. In time, these taxes and deductions were progressively reduced until January 25, 1827, when all taxes and levies on the cultivation, production and domestic consumption of tobacco were dropped; only a small royalty on leaf and rolled tobacco exports was kept. This decision proved to be extremely beneficial for Cuba's blooming cigar industry and a new era of expansion ensued.

To have an idea of what the abolition of the monopoly in 1817 and the ban on taxes in 1827 meant for the national tobacco production, it is helpful to compare the area of land that was dedicated to tobacco between those two years and the area under cultivation twenty years later, in 1846. According to official records, 13,899 hectares were planted with tobacco in 1817; ten years later, that figure had risen only to 18,640. But in 1846 tobacco lands had slightly more than doubled to 37,589 hectares.

Throughout the rest of the 19th Century, the cultivation of tobacco continued to grow steadily, except during the last years of the nineties, when the war for independence substantially affected all the Cuban plantations. The pace was again picked up in the initial years of this century, and eventually tobacco became one of the nation's main staples, a characteristic that remains unchanged to this day.

The famous Habanensis variety of tobacco was developed at the beginning of the 1900's at a time that Cuba had enough tobacco under cultivation.

# TRADITIONAL VARIETIES

There is very little information on the varieties of tobacco that were cultivated in Cuba since pre-Columbian days to the present century except for a few incomplete descriptions that leave out their names and fundamental characteristics. What is really known for fact is that plantations were very heterogenous as ers themselves. They used to harvest the main plant and after the first, second or even third sprouting did they collect the seeds, without any consideration as to the fundamental traits of the original plant, let alone the differences that might exist between the plants whose sprouts had generated the seeds.

**The typical *Criollo* plantations in which one of Cuba's most popular tobacco varieties is grown. These vegas (areas in which tobaccos are grown) are in the finest tobacco-growing lands in the world in the Vuelta Abajo in Pinar del Rio Province.**

a result of the inadequate seed production system, which was made at random without any selection whatsoever of the plants that were earmarked for seed, nor was there any awareness of the need to isolate those plants to prevent undesirable crossings of different strains. Throughout this long period of time, seeds were generally produced by the tobacco farm-

This made it impossible to have genetically pure tobacco varieties to guarantee the required uniformity of the plantations and the necessary stability of the yields and quality of the produce. In spite of this, Cuban tobacco won early fame as the best in the world, and not even when new seeds from other countries were introduced into the Cuban plantations did the leaves from the island cease to be the most highly regarded of all. This shows the all-important role of the climate and the particular characteristics of the Cuban soils, which give black tobacco a distinctive quality that sets it apart from the ones harvested anywhere in the world.

Nevertheless, it must be pointed out that if genetically stable strains of genuine native black tobacco are combined with Cuba's extraordinary natural conditions for the growing of this plant, the results must necessarily be superior, raising the quality of the product to inimitable standards. That is why, since the first decade of this century, a considerable attention was given to the identification and preservation of the original Cuban varieties, as well as to the development of new and equally good strains.

In 1907, an American researcher working in Cuba, H.Hasselbring, took Cuban seeds to the United States in order to study the behavior of those varieties in another climate and under totally different cultivation conditions. In the tobacco plantations developed from those seeds, he observed a striking diversity which he initially thought was a possible effect of the climatic change. The following year, Hasselbring planted the same seeds on the grounds of the former Agricultural Station in Santiago de las Vegas, very near Havana, and again observed the same phenotypic diversity that characterized the Cuban plantations of the times. He concluded that this heterogeniety was the result of an indiscriminate mixing of seeds from different varieties of tobacco and from the various hybrid forms that already existed.

**A view of the Criollo tobacco growing in the sun. This area is the Guanes in Pinar del Rio.**

**The variety known as *Pelo de Oro* which is grown in the central and eastern tobacco growing regions of Cuba.**

Henceforward, the researcher undertook to select - from amongst the mosaic of existing varieties - a single example that would represent the genuine Cuban black tobacco. Hasselbring resorted to the counsel of numerous well-experienced tobacco growers who described to him what they considered to be the real and original black tobacco plant. After some time he was able to isolate a considerably uniform plant which he dubbed "Habanensis". This "Habanensis" variety was eventually cultivated on a relatively large scale, but never enough to consider it fully generalized.

A few years later, in 1918, the outstanding Cuban scientist, Don Tomás Roig, repeated Hasselbring's experiences but this time with the help of 200 small tobacco producers who gave him an invaluable asssistance in the selection of a "new and purified variety", which showed a great uniformity and had very good agricultural and organoleptic qualities. This variety was presented as the true representative of Cuban black tobacco and fully satisfied the market's demands. However, although this variety got to be cultivated to a larger scale than Hasselbring's "Habanensis", it was never completely generalized and by the end of the thirties, the Cuban plantations were again a veritable collection of varieties with the consequent loss of quality and yields of the theretofore exclusive type of tobacco plant being grown in Cuba.

In 1937, the first Experimental Tobacco Station was founded in San Juán y Martínez, in the province of Pinar del Río. One of the very first tasks of this station was to select from the existing heterogeneus varieties a single kind of black tobacco which would fully comply with the distinctive traits of the famous and

Vega del Sol en Palo with a rich growth of *Criollo* in Pinar del Rio, the world's best cigar tobacco region.

highly priced Cuban black tobacco. In 1940, after three years of hard work, the present commercial variety named "Criollo" was finally developed and it fulfilled every requirement to make an "Habano" a unique product for its indisputable and matchless organoleptic quality.

The "Criollo" variety has a potential mean yield of about 1900 kilos per hectare, its shoots are numerous and well developed and its average height with inflorescence is 1.75 meters. The plant normally carries 16 usable leaves, set 7cm apart, and its largest leaf is aproximately 27 cm wide and 43 cm long. It is resistant to the black-shank, but highly vulnerable to the blue mould and the tobacco mosaic virus (TMV). At present it is used as a commercial variety and cultivated in open sunshine in Pinar del Río.

In the thirties, a few years before the introduction of the "Criollo" as a commercial variety, Pinar del Río began to grow a new variety known as "Pelo de Oro" (Golden Hair). The origin of this variety is uncertain. Some say it was brought over from Mexico by the **Cuban Land & Tobacco Leaf Co.**, that used to own large tobacco plantations in the San Juán Y Martínez zone, while others believe it is the result of natural cross-breeding between some of the Cuban black tobacco strains and the Middle East "Esmirna" variety that was grown in small quantities in Pinar del Río.

Regardless of its origins and in spite of its excellent organoleptic quality, the "Pelo de Oro" variety is different from the original black tobacco of Cuba and was therefore never established as a commercial variety in the world famous "Vuelta Abajo" region. But the "Pelo de Oro" was nonetheless grown with considerable success in the central region of Cuba, known as Remedio, and soon expanded over to the eastern part of the island, Vuelta Arriba, where it became the main commercial tobacco variety to this day.

**This vega is covered with cheese cloth to protect the plants from the sun and insects. This shade-grown tobacco is basically used for *capa* or *wrapper* as it is called in English.**

**This plantation is growing the *corojo* variety of cigar tobacco. It has been used in Cuba for *capa* (=wrapper) since 1947 for high quality Havana cigars.**

The leaves of the "Pelo de Oro", aside from their distinctive high quality, mature with great uniformity which permits their collection in bunches. This variety produces an outstanding number of wrapper leaves allowing three and even four gleanings from a single plant; this raises its production potential to about 2300 kg/hectare. On average, it gives 12 to 14 usable leaves per plant, set 8 cm apart, and the largest leaf is normally 25cm wide and 45 cm long. The "Pelo de Oro is resistant to the black-shank, but highly vulnerable to the blue mould and the "orobanche", a parasitic plant that wreaks havoc in the regions where this tobacco variety is cultivated.

In the early forties, Daniel Rodríguez, one of the leading tobacco producers in Pinar del Río, hired a Dutch botanist named Nienhuys to develop a new variety that would preserve all the virtues of the Cuban black tobacco but that would also produce excellent wrapper leaves. Rodríguez launched an improvement program based on cross-breeding "Criollo" strains with a good wrapper producing "Sumatra" variety. After long years of testing, Rodríguez and Niehuys obtained the present commercial variety "Corojo", named after the farm where it was initially developed.

The "Corojo" variety is noted for its superb wrapper leaves, which constitute the distinguishing mark of Cuban rolled cigars, known the world over as "Havanas". This variety yields some 2000 kg/hectare, with 20 per cent of this produce in high quality wrapper leaves. It gives 16 to 18 usable leaves per plant, set 10 cm apart; its height, including inflorescence, is 2.07 m. The central leaves are 28 to 30 cm wide and 48 to 50 cm long. It produces abundant shoots but it is only moderately resistant to the black-shank and highly vulnerable to the blue mould and the mosaic virus.

GPF
HABANA
TOMAS GUTIERREZ
LA IMPERIOSA
HABANA
HABANA
ROMEO Y JULIE
SAN SEBASTIAN
HABANA
ROMEO Y JULIET
SAN SEBASTIAN
W
1914
FINEST SELECTED
SUPER CORONAS
HABANA
BELINDA - HABANA

# MAIN NATURAL ENEMIES

From the time before the discovery of America and up until the 19th century, insects were the main natural enemies of the tobacco plant in Cuba. The greatest damage was caused by *Heliothis virescens* Fabricius (commonly known in Cuba as the "cogollero del tabaco" and in the US as the "budworm," for its habit of feeding mainly on the leaves of the apical bud of the plant), which has been, since remote times, the most important tobacco pest in Cuba. Control of *Heliothis* has always had to be manual, as in the olden days, or by a combination of chemical and biological products which, in the absence of genetically resistant varieties, is the most effective and economical form of control.

It was not until early in this century that a new enemy began to make itself felt in Cuban tobacco plantations, this time a fungus, *Phytophthora parasitica var. nicotianae* (Brenda de Haan) Turker which, as we have said, causes one of the diseases with the greatest economic impact on national tobacco production due to the extensive damage it can do both in seed beds and plantations. The disease is commonly known in Cuba as "pata prieta" (black shank) or "mancha negra" because of the characteristic symptoms that appear on the diseased plant. The base of the stalk grows dark as a result of the necrosis of the local tissue, or when heavy rains splash the spores of the fungus onto the leaves, there may appear dark spots on the lower leaves of the adult plant or on the seedlings.

*P. parasitica* is a semi-aquatic soil fungus that is easily spread by irrigation water or by rain, which makes it particularly difficult to control. In the seed beds, disinfection of the soil and regular applications of fungicides provide acceptable control levels, but in the plantations, chemical control of the disease is economically prohibitive. Thus, the most expedient way of minimizing the damage this disease can cause in years that are climatically favorable to its development is the use of resistant varieties.

All the soils in Cuba planted with tobacco are contaminated with *P. parasitica* to a greater or less extent, so that the use of susceptible varieties, much sooner than later, invariably results in the total destruction of the plantation. Furthermore, continued cultivation of tobacco in those areas where for different reasons crop rotation cannot be practiced inevitably leads to an increased infec-

**A tobacco plant suffering from *black shank* disease which is caused by the fungus parasite *Phytophthora parasitica* var. *nicotianae*.**

This tobacco plant is being attacked by the parasitic plant known in English as the *broomrape.* Scientifically it is called *Orobanche ramosa* Linnaeus. It is a succulent and appears in January, thus forcing farmers to plant much earlier.

tion potential in the soils to the point where only the most resistant varieties can survive. In these cases, varieties such as "Corojo," which have only a medium resistance to this disease, wind up being practically destroyed, especially in hot, rainy years. This was the case in the 1989-90 season, when a great many covered tobacco plantations in Pinar del Rio province were totally destroyed.

*Orobanche ramosa* L., a parasitic plant commonly known in English as broomrape, has over the years become a very important enemy of tobacco plantations in Cuba. This succulent plant causes great losses, both in agricultural yields and in the quality of the tobacco harvested in Havana and in the central provinces of the country. In these areas, the soils are strongly contaminated with the minute seeds of the parasite and tobacco cultivation is practically impossible if the planting is not done very early so that when broomrape appears in January it cannot greatly affect the development of the tobacco plant. So far, there are no reports of the existence of *Nicotiana* varieties or species resistant to this parasite, so it has not been possible to implement genetic improvement programs to produce resistant commercial varieties.

Some time in the middle of this century, the effects of another great enemy of tobacco production in Cuba, the tobacco mosaic virus (TMV) began to be felt. TMV causes the disease known to planters in Pinar del Rio as "macho," which causes important losses in the provinces of Havana and Pinar del Rio. There is no known effective chemical agent to control it, but fortunately, resistant gene banks do exist making it possible to implement

**This plantation with fine *Corojo* wrapper tobacco was destroyed by *Orobanche.***

This malady known as TMV or *tobacco mosaic virus* has attacked this plantation. The tobacco farmers in Pinar del Rio and Havana call this disease *macho*.

genetic improvement programs to develop resistant commercial varieties. The tobacco mosaic virus does not have vectors, as such, but is spread mechanically, mostly by man himself. When workers are in the fields or in the tobacco houses performing any of the customary cultural jobs, such as debudding and others, they may brush up against an infected plant and continue their work without disinfecting their hands and thus spread the disease over a large part of the plantation.

**This vega (plantation) was destroyed by blue mold, *Peronospora tabacina* Adam. It first appeared in Cuba in 1957 and it almost annihilated the crop in Partido, in the province of Havana.**

Blue mold (*Peronospora tabacina* Adam) made its first appearance in Cuba in 1957. This disease, along with black shank, is one of the greatest enemies of Cuban tobacco. When it first struck, in 1957, it produced great losses, particularly in the area of Partido, Havana province, but it disappeared the next year and did not return until 1979, when it turned up again and destroyed about 95% of the national tobacco harvest. From that moment on it has been present year after year requiring constant use of fungicides to be able to continue planting the traditional varieties, all highly susceptible to the fungus.

*P. tabacina* is an airborne fungus that spreads easily and rapidly. When the weather is favorable for its development (cool cloudy days with light rains) it can devastate huge areas of tobacco plantations in just two or three days if the relevant measures are not implemented. For this disease, the most effective treatment has usually been the fungicide sold under the Ridomil trademark. It is highly effective and has made it possible to continue growing tobacco in Cuba after the reappear-

A close-up of a tobacco plant suffering from the blue mold, *Peronospora tabacina.*

*Criollo* which almost paralyzed tobacco production in some area because of the blue mold. This is an example of *Criollo* suffering from blue mold, *Peronospora tabacina*.

This plantation of *Corojo* was attacked and destroyed by black shank disease caused by the fungus *Phytophthora parasitica* var. *nicotianae*. Known in Cuba as either *mancha negra* or *pata prieta*.

This nice *Corojo* type cigar tobacco plant was destroyed by the blue mold.

ance of blue mold. However, in recent years, resistant strains of blue mold have been appearing and they pose a grave danger to the national tobacco industry if new resistant black tobacco varieties are not developed soon, with the same organoleptic qualities as the traditional varieties to be able to use them in their stead, especially for late planting, which is where the blue mold does the greatest damage.

There are other diseases that affect tobacco in Cuba during its agricultural phase, but they have not had any great economic impact because the varieties traditionally planted, "Criollo," "Pelo de Oro" and "Corojo," are more or less resistant to them and the negative impact has never gone beyond the normally tolerable limits. However, in the case of new varieties, it is very important to bear in mind that these diseases do exist in the country, or there will be danger of serious damage if they are commercially planted.

**The brown leafspot disease is produced by the fungus *Alternaria tenuis* Nees. It does damage by producing small spots on the leaves which ruins the leaf for use as wrapper.**

One of the most important of these diseases is the one known as brown leaf spot, produced by *Alternaria tenuis* Nees. This fungus generally does some damage to the traditional varieties by producing small spots on the leaves. These spots are economically harmful only in the case of covered tobacco for wrapper leaf. The wrapper leaf is virtually useless, as such, if it is spotted, so that *Alternaria* can cause lower yields in wrapper production. However, in the case of susceptible varieties, the spots grow together forming large brown

This tobacco leaf is suffering from an environmental disease variously referred to as *environmental necrosis* or *weather fleck.* It is brought on by high concentrations of ozone in the air.

areas that ripen the leaf prematurely and kill it. With favorable humidity and temperature conditions, the spots can grow quickly invading the entire plantation in a very brief period of time and destroying it almost completely. This disease is most aggressive toward the end of the agricultural season making it practically impossible to grow susceptible varieties in Cuba during that period.

The other disease that can be included in this group is "environmental necrosis" or "weather-fleck," brought on by high concentrations of ozone in the lower strata of the atmosphere. This anomaly is characterized by a profusion of small white spots on the leaf. In resistant varieties, the effects are usually limited to the lower leaves, but in susceptible varieties it can cover all the leaves and ultimately kill the plant. When the attack is severe, the leaves are totally useless for the cigar industry and losses may be considerable. In Cuba it is practically impossible to plant varieties that are not resistant to environmental necrosis, especially in covered tobacco, which is where the disease is most aggressive.

The main enemy affecting seedlings is Damping-off, produced by several species of the genus *Pythium* and two fungi, *Rhizoctonia solani* Kuhn and *P. parasitica*. This disease is typically found in seed beds, that is, it attacks the plant during its earliest stage of development when its genetic resistance has yet to take hold. Thus, planters cannot trust genetics and must use fungicides.

Lastly, we have the warehouse pests. The most important is an insect, *Lasioderma serricorne* Fab., also known as the cigar beetle (or cigarette beetle in the US). This insect feeds on the dry leaves during storage or in the finished product, both cigars and cigarettes. In both its larval and adult stages, *Lasioderma* attacks dry tobacco leaf producing a great number of small holes thereby damaging the quality of the leaf or making the finished product useless. Wrapper leaf attacked by this insect cannot be used for wrapper at all.

*Lasioderma* can be controlled by regular fumigation of the stored products with a variety of chemical agents. For small quantities of tobacco, and especially for finished cigars, some consumers use a very practical method, which is to store the product at -20°C for a period of 48 hours. This helps the cigars keep for a year or more without the need for chemical fumigation.

**From the time before Columbus visited Cuba until the 10th century, insects were the main cause of crop failures. The greatest damage was done by the *cogollero del tabaco*, which is known scientifically as *Heliothis virescens*. In English the insect is known as the *budworm*.**

PUNCH HABANA
MANUEL LOPEZ
HABANA
PUNCH
SPECIALLY SELECTED FOR
PUNCH
HABANA
SPECIALLY MADE FOR
PUNCH
HABANA
JOHN MORGAN & SONS LTD.
HABANA
HABANA
SPECIALLY SELECTED
PUNCH
FOR FRIBOURG & TREYER
HABANA
HABANA
PUNCH
R.E.
HABANA
MANUEL LOPEZ
HABANA
RIO VISTA
PUNCH
HABANA
PUNCH
SANTIAGO
CHILE
PUNCH
CLUB DE LA UNION
SANTIAGO
HABANA

# NEWLY DEVELOPED VARIETIES

The genetic improvement program instituted in 1959 at the San Juán y Martínez Experimental Station to produce new Cuban varieties of black tobacco was based on the following selection criteria: yield potential, quality and resistance to black shank. In other words, when the program got under way, the only objective was to produce new varieties that were better than the traditional varieties in yield, but had the same quality and resistance capability against black shank. After 15 years of work, a new black tobacco variety, "Habano Ligero," was produced. It is characterized by a yield potential of over 2,400 kg/ha, an average of 22 useful leaves per plant, slight development of the axillary buds and a high degree of resistance to black shank. However, the organoleptic quality of the leaves (aroma, strength and taste) were not up to the standards of the Havana Cigar market and it had to be left for the production of leaf for the domestic cigarette industry.

Some time later, early in the 80's, a variety known as "Cabaiguan-72," produced at the Cabaiguan Experimental Station in Sancti Spiritus Province, was liberated for planting. As in the case of "Habano Ligero," it was resistant to black shank and had a high production potential, but it too was not up to the standards of the Havana Cigar market and also had to be left exclusively for the cigarette industry.

**"Escambray-70" was the first Cuban black tobacco which developed a resistance to both black shank and tobacco mosaic virus. It was developed as part of the program for genetic improvement initiated in 1959 at the San Juan Martinez Experimental Station. This station was charged with developing new strains of Cuban black tobacco which had greater yield, high quality and resistance to black shank and other diseases.**

**In 1988 a Cuban tobacco destined for fine cigars was developed which was resistant to blue mold, black shank and TMV. It was called *Habana P.R.***

NA-P.R.

The *Habana-2000* variety, shown here, is highly resistant to blue mold, black shank and environmental necrosis. It yields about 2,200 kg (almost 5,000 pounds) per hectare (one hectare is 2.471 acres) and a quarter of that is fine wrapper (capa).

Also in the 80's, the genetic improvement program at the Experimental Station of San Antonio de los Baños, Havana Province, came up with a new variety known as "Escambray-70." This was the first Cuban black tobacco variety that was resistant to black shank and TMV, had a high production potential (2,200 kg/ha), and good quality, but it produced a large number of shoots, which makes it difficult and expensive to use commercially, so much so that it was not accepted as a commercial variety. What it has been used for is as a source of genes for the different genetic improvement programs.

The reappearance of blue mold in Cuba in 1979 forced the country to direct all of its efforts at finding varieties that were resistant to this disease, as well as black shank and, if possible, TMV. It also had to have a high production potential, produce few shoots and have organoleptic qualities equal to those of the traditional varieties.

**The author inspects plantings of Habana-2000 in San Luis, Pinar del Rio.**

In 1988, the first program, which began in 1981, finally produced a variety ("Habana P.R.") that was resistant to blue mold, black shank and TMV. This variety also has a yield potential around 2,200 kg/ha, a high production of superior grades and good organoleptic qualities. It is characterized by scant production of shoots (less than the traditional varieties) and the excellent reddish colors the leaves acquire after drying.

These Habana-2000 plants were allowed to flower and seed. Each flower produces a seed pod which contains hundreds of tiny black seeds the size of ground pepper.

In tests to show the resistance to blue mold, two varieties are tested at the same time: the center rows are Habana-2000 while the rows on the sides are Corojo.

In 1992, a second program aimed at turning out varieties for the production of wrapper leaf achieved two new commercial varieties whose general characteristics were very similar to those of the traditional varieties, but with much better resistance to diseases and a higher yield potential. They were called "Habana-92" and "Habana-2000."

The "Habana-2000" variety is highly resistant to blue mold, black shank and environmental necrosis. When it is cultivated in the conditions obtaining in the farms of private tobacco producers in Pinar del Rio Province, its yield is in the vicinity of 2,200 kg/ha and about 25% of the leaf is high quality wrapper. It produces around 18 useful leaves per plant, with physical and chemical characteristics similar to those of the traditional "Corojo" variety. It develops only the higher axillary

To test the resistance of the popular tobaccos to blue mold, a row of each variety was planted and subjected to the same conditions. All were adversely affected except the Habana-92.

Research on Cuban cigar tobacco continues to make great strides in protection from disease, insects and weather. Thus far the multi-purpose Habana-92 is the best of the new varieties.

**Above: This section of a Habana-92 plantation was attacked by *Orobanche ramosa*. The section in the rear stayed free of the parasite.**
**Below: Habana-92 tobacco plants purposely exposed to *Orobanche ramosa* to test various defenses.**

**Above: Habana-92 being shade grown in a provincial Havana farm.**
**Below: Habana-92 being grown in the sun in San Juan City, Pinar del Rio, Cuba where conditions are excellent for the cultivation of this variety.**

A plantation of the Habana-92 variety in Pinar del Rio City, in Pinar del Rio province.

HABANA-92

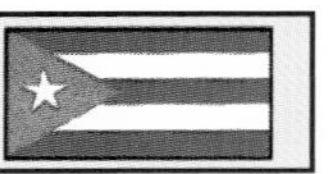

The Habanera-92 being grown on the open field in the sun, Guane, Pinar del Rio. At this time the leaves were being removed in pairs (*mancuernas).*

Young plants of Habana-92 in a large plantation in Central Cuba. Note how closely planted this crop is.

buds, thereby making its cultivation easier and more economical, because as opposed to the "Corojo" variety, which requires four or five "debudding" passes, "Habana-2000" can get by with only two or three passes. The dry leaves of this variety have an attractive and uniform light brown color and the veins are thin.

Furthermore, "Habana-2000" is, so far, the most complete Cuban black tobacco variety from all points of view. It has a very high level of resistance against blue mold, black shank, brown spot of the leaves and environmental necrosis. It is also highly tolerant of *Orobanche*, for which no other resistant variety has been reported anywhere in the world. Its production capability is around 2,200 kg/ha; its high quality wrapper yield is higher than the original "Corojo" variety and its superior class yield is much higher than the original "Criollo" variety, when it is grown using

These Habana-92 plants are being grown only for their capa (wrapper) in the open field in San Luis, Pinar del Rio. The leaves not suitable for wrapper are used for other purposes.

the "sol ensartado" system. It produces few shoots, which makes it easier and more economical to cultivate because it requires less labor. The technical ripeness of its leaves is sufficiently uniform and this makes it possible to harvest it by **"mancuernas,"**[1] with the ensuing yield benefits stemming from the possibility of using the **"capaduras."**[2]

From the above description we can deduce that this is a highly adaptable variety, that is, it can be used in the different conditions in which black tobacco is cultivated in Cuba, a characteristic that no other variety, not even the traditional ones, have. Lastly, "Habana-92" has another quality in its favor: its high tolerance to irregularities in its cultivation. As the farmers say, it waits for you to perform the different culture tasks without decreasing its yield or its quality.

**Sun planted field planted with Habana-92 in the city of Cabaiguan, province of Sancti Spiritus.**

*1 Part of the tobacco plant with a pair of leaves attached.*

*2 Leaves produced after the harvest of the principal leaves.*

**This Habana-92 plantation is basically for producing seeds. It is shade grown to protect the flowers from being cross-fertilized from pollen of a different variety.**

The dry leaves, harvested by any one of the systems currently being used in Cuba for the production of black tobacco, always have a lively and uniform reddish-brown color. They characteristically have a high fat content; they are very elastic, have thin veins and excellent organoleptic qualities. For all of these reasons, "Habana-92" may be considered the first multi-purpose variety produced in Cuba and capable of being planted in almost any tobacco producing area in the country.

Below: This is a new variety of black cigar tobacco called *Habana Vuelta Arriba*. grown in the sun in the central and eastern part of Cuba. It is a high producer and is very resistant to blue mold.

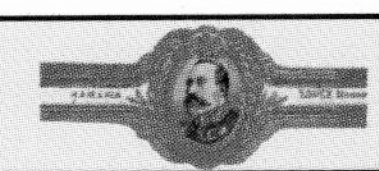

# METHODS OF CULTIVATION AND HARVESTING

The earliest information available on the way tobacco was cultivated in Cuba in the past century is found in an article by Dr. Antonio L. Valverde, published in 1915 in the magazine *Reforma Social* with the title *El Estanco del tabaco en Cuba* (The Tobacco Monopoly in Cuba). The author refers to a group of instructions issued by the Factory to all tobacco farmers before 1817, which clearly define the standard phyto-technical principles of the times.

This is a traditional plantation with sun-grown black tobacco. the buds have been removed so the plants won't flower.

Above: Oxen are used to assist the farmers in tending their young, sun grown tobacco plants.

Left: Removing the suckers is very important to the size and strength of the tobacco plant. The suckers must be removed at exactly the right time.

These practical instructions or recommendations underlined the convenience of not planting too many seeds on the furrows to avoid overpopulation and the consequent weakening of the shoots. The sowing season was best begun on October 15 and should extend no further than late January. The ideal distance between plants was 85 cm, while rows were to be 105 cm apart. Suckers had to be removed early on and the shoots had to be cut off three or four times before they reached 5 cm. The harvest began when the plants reached their full maturity. They strongly spoke against the age-old custom of uprooting the plants and laying them to dry in the barns. The proper method was the one practiced by the farmers in Havana, who picked the leaves one by one, starting with the top two and continued down the plant, picking two leaves each time at 8 day intervals.

According to the *Cartilla Agraria para el Cultivo del Tabaco* (Agrarian Primer for the Cultivation of Tobacco), published by Tomás Salazar in 1850, the phytotechnic procedures that were being applied in tobacco at that moment were somewhat different from the ones described previously. The most substantial changes had taken place in the planting distances; he reccomended 84 cm between rows and 63 cm between plants. The pair-on-stem harvesting method had become standardized, having already displaced the uprooting of the entire plant. Four or five of each plant's pairs of leaves had to be debudded, which made the plants grow to heights ranging from 84 to 120 cm. The largest leaves were longer than 84 cm and their width about one third of the length.

Left: Growing and harvesting tobacco is back-breaking work. The leaves are removed two at a time in most cases.

Below: The tobacco leaves which are harvested in pairs cut at the same time enable the farmer to place them over rods which will be brought to the drying barns. When capa (wrapper) leaves are picked leaf-by-leaf, one at a time, they must be sewn together so they can be draped over the drying rods.

At present, the techniques used in the cultivation of Cuban black tobacco are in keeping with the agronomical peculiarities of the varieties introduced since 1940 and with the potential yields of the soils dedicated to that crop. However, the principles that rule the present techniques are essentially the same as the ones traditionally applied in the cultivation of tobacco in Cuba.

In the initial years of this century, the technique of covering the tobacco plants with cheese-cloth (shade grown or covered tobacco), was introduced in Cuba to obtain wrapper leaves with a better color and texture than ones produced until then in the open sunshine plantations. Mr. Calixto López was the first to use the cheese-cloth covers at his farm **Guainacabo**, in the municipality of San Luís, Pinar del Río province. Shortly after that, Don Luís Marx adopted this system at his farm **Zorrilla**, near the town of Alquizar, in the Partido region.

Simultaneously, the tobacco Trust also applied this method in some of its Vuelta Abajo farms, after which most of the leading tobacco growers of the country - except the Vuelta Arriba farmers - followed suit. Together with the covered cultivation method, the leaf by leaf picking was also introduced in the Partido region, eliminating the cutting in pairs. The loose leaves were now sewn together and hung to dry from wooden staffs. This new procedure soon included the open sunshine tobacco harvested in that region and in the best plantations of Vuelta Abajo.

It is therefore safe to say that since the first decade of this century Cuban black tobacco was grown under the three agricultural regimes that are still applied to this day. These regimes are designed to produce tobacco for different industrial uses (wrapper, binder, filler and pipe tobacco), and each is known in Cuba as "sunshine tobacco on staffs", "sown sunshine tobacco" and "covered tobacco".

The "sunshine tobacco on staffs" is the black tobacco cultivated under full sunshine conditions whose leaves are harvested in pairs. This is done by progressively cutting the stem of the plant in sections that contain two or three leaves, depending on their dimensions. When the plant reaches the optimal technical maturity, harvesting begins by cutting the top part of the stem that contains the last two or three leaves of the plant. This is done several times until the lower section with two or three leaves is finally cut. This method also permits the harvesting of "capaduras", which are the leaves that reappear from the shoots of the principal plant after harvesting. The sections of stem or "mancuernas" are placed on wooden staffs and placed in the curing barns to dry. This tobacco is generally used as filler and binder for manufacturing cigars for the domestic market, for leaf tobacco exports and for the national cigarrette industry. About 30% of the black tobacco that is grown today in Pinar del Río and more than 90% of the type produced in the central and eastern regions of Cuba fall into that category.

On the other hand, "sewn sunshine tobacco" is also cultivated under full sunshine conditions but harvested leaf by leaf. This method consists of picking first the lower

leaves of the plant and proceeding upwards along the stem when the leaves successively reach their optimal maturity. The two or three leaves that mature simultaneously are picked manually, so in five "pickings", at 7 to 8 day intervals, all the leaves of a single plant are collected. The leaves are immediately sewn together with an appropiate string or thread using a specially designed needle. All the tobacco of the premium plantations of Pinar del Río is grown and harvested according to this method and it is basically used as binder and filler in the manufacture of Havanas or, in the case of the choice plantation produce, for leaf-tobacco exports and as raw material for the national cigar and cigarrette industries.

Lastly, "shade grown" or "covered tobacco" is the one grown under cheese-cloth covers. Sunlight has a great influence on the texture and elasticity of the leaves, as well as on the intensity and uniformity of their color; by regulating their exposure to direct sunlight, the plants produce excellent wrapper leaves that show very thin veins. In general, covered tobacco is less exposed to the attack by insects and the destructive effects of the weather, like strong winds, heavy rainfall and sleet. At the present time, all the tobacco of the Partido zone, in the province of Havana, is cultivated under cloth, as well as a considerable part of the tobacco grown in the San Juán y Martínez and San Luís municipalities in Pinar del Río. The tobacco leaves grown by this method are hand picked one by one and then sewn together for drying. In this case, six to eight "pickings" are done, depending on the number of leaves that were left on the plant when unbudded. All the wrapper leaves used in the manufacture of Habanos come from different varieties of Cuban black tobacco specifically developed for this purpose and cultivated by the covered method.

Workers carrying leaves which were cut individually from the plants.

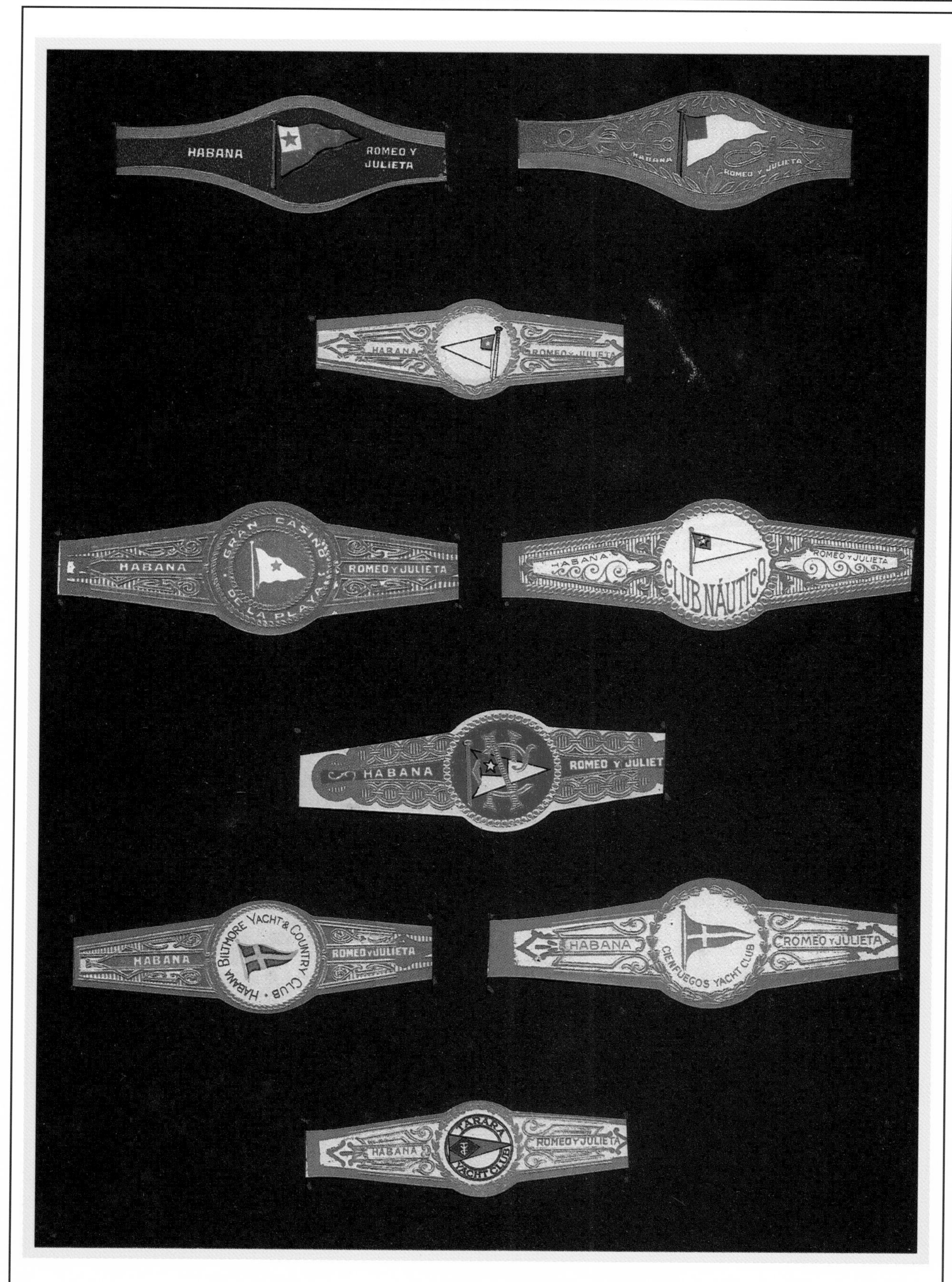
HABANA
ROMEO Y JULIETA
HABANA
ROMEO Y JULIETA
HABANA
ROMEO Y JULIETA
GRAN CASINO DE LA PLAYA
HABANA
ROMEO Y JULIETA
CLUB NÁUTICO
HABANA
ROMEO Y JULIETA
HABANA
ROMEO Y JULIET
HABANA BILTMORE YACHT & COUNTRY CLUB
HABANA
ROMEO Y JULIETA
CIENFUEGOS YACHT CLUB
HABANA
ROMEO Y JULIETA
TARARA YACHT CLUB
HABANA
ROMEO Y JULIETA

# PRE-INDUSTRIAL PROCEDURES

Once the harvest is completed, be it by the leaf by leaf or the pair-on-stem methods, the leaves are stored in the curing barns for 45 to 60 day periods, which is the time required for their total dessecation. This drying procedure of Cuban black tobacco is traditionally performed in a natural way, that is, exposed to the prevailing weather conditions without any form of artificial regulation.

Dried tobacco undergoes a first stage of fermentation in the curing barns, when the leaves are carefully stacked in piles of variable dimensions called "pilones", forming a rectangular, compact mass of tobacco leaves. These piles, properly covered with plantain leaves, cheese-cloth or other suitable materials, hold the tobacco leaves for about 30 days until they reach the proper degree of fermentation. After that, the leaves are taken to the sorting and classification workshops, where they receive a second period of natural fermentation in very similar conditions to the one previously described. When this second stage is over, the leaves are sorted out and classified according to their particular characteristics.

**Throughout the tobacco growing areas in Cuba you can see these typical curing barns. The walls and roof are made of palm leaves because the palm leaves are easy and inexpensive to obtain and last a long time. They are also ideal for tobacco curing.**

More modern curing barns are those made of more permanent materials such as wood, corrugated iron or concrete. Most black tobacco is now cured in these permanent barns.

The most modern curing barns are much larger and are made of concrete. These barns are typical of the wrapper (capa) processing barns in Havana province.

In the case of tobacco cultivated under cheese-cloth, the classification takes into account basic features of the leaf like color, texture, gloss, size, elasticity and the flaws or overall damages it may show. Thus, more than 50 different classes are sorted out and only the very best are used as wrapper for the world famous Habanos cigars. These wrapper leaves must have the right color, ranging from light brown to very light brown; reddish brown leaves are also admitted, but in all cases their color has to be uniform and glossy. The leaves must be either thin or slightly thin, with tenuous veins, elastic and adequately oily. They must be flawless, but if they show any damages, these can only be found near the central nerve, in order not to affect the part of the leaf

In the curing barns, farmers sew the leaves which are individually cut from the plant, so they can be hung on drying rods as shown in the background of this photo.

**After the harvesting of the tobacco leaves, they are hung in sheds or barns to dry, as seen above. Once they are dried, the farmers in various regions have their efforts evaluated as the bundles are shipped to the factories.**

After being counted and weighed the bundles are taken to a warehouse for further processing.

This is a typical *matul* or bundle harvested *a mancuernas*. Each bundle contains the leaves dried on one *cuje*. The *cuje* is the wooden rod upon which the tobacco is hung during the drying process.

The *matules* or bundles are being moved from the curing barn to the warehouse in which the second fermenting stage will take place.

used as wrapper. Their dimensions may vary, but size determines in what type of cigar will a specific wrapper be used.

Tobacco grown in the fine plantations of Vuelta Abajo, where the filler and binder material for Habanos are produced, is divided into four categories or "timings", according to the position occupied by the leaves on the plant and their distinctive characteristics. These are:

Volado (filler). The three or four lowest leaves on the plant. Normally thin, soft textured, low on nicotin and aromatic, they burn very easily. These constitute the Strength No.1.

Seco (dry). Leaves coming from the central section of the plant. Very good texture, very aromatic withmedium nicotine content, they burn easily. These constitute the Strength No.2.

Ligero (light). The two or three leaves immediately below the top two on the plant. Noted for their coarse texture, high nicotine content and strong taste. These constitute the Strength No.3.

Medio Tiempo (mid-term). The top two leaves that crown the plant. Very coarse texture, difficult to burn, very high nicotine content and extremely strong taste. These constitute the Strength No. 4.

After completing its second fermentation period, the tobacco that comes from fine plantations is sorted out into classes according to texture, size and damage levels. More than 30 different classes are recognized, but only those that fall into the categories or "timings" previously described are used as filler and binder for Havanas.

Once selected, each class of tobacco is individually packed into bales and, depending

**The first stage of fermentation may be when the dried tobacco are packed in *pilones* which are covered variably with plantain leaves, cheese cloth or potato sacking. This first fermentation stage lasts about one month. Various fermentation processes, especially when water is added, can bring the temperature to 50°C (over 120°F).**

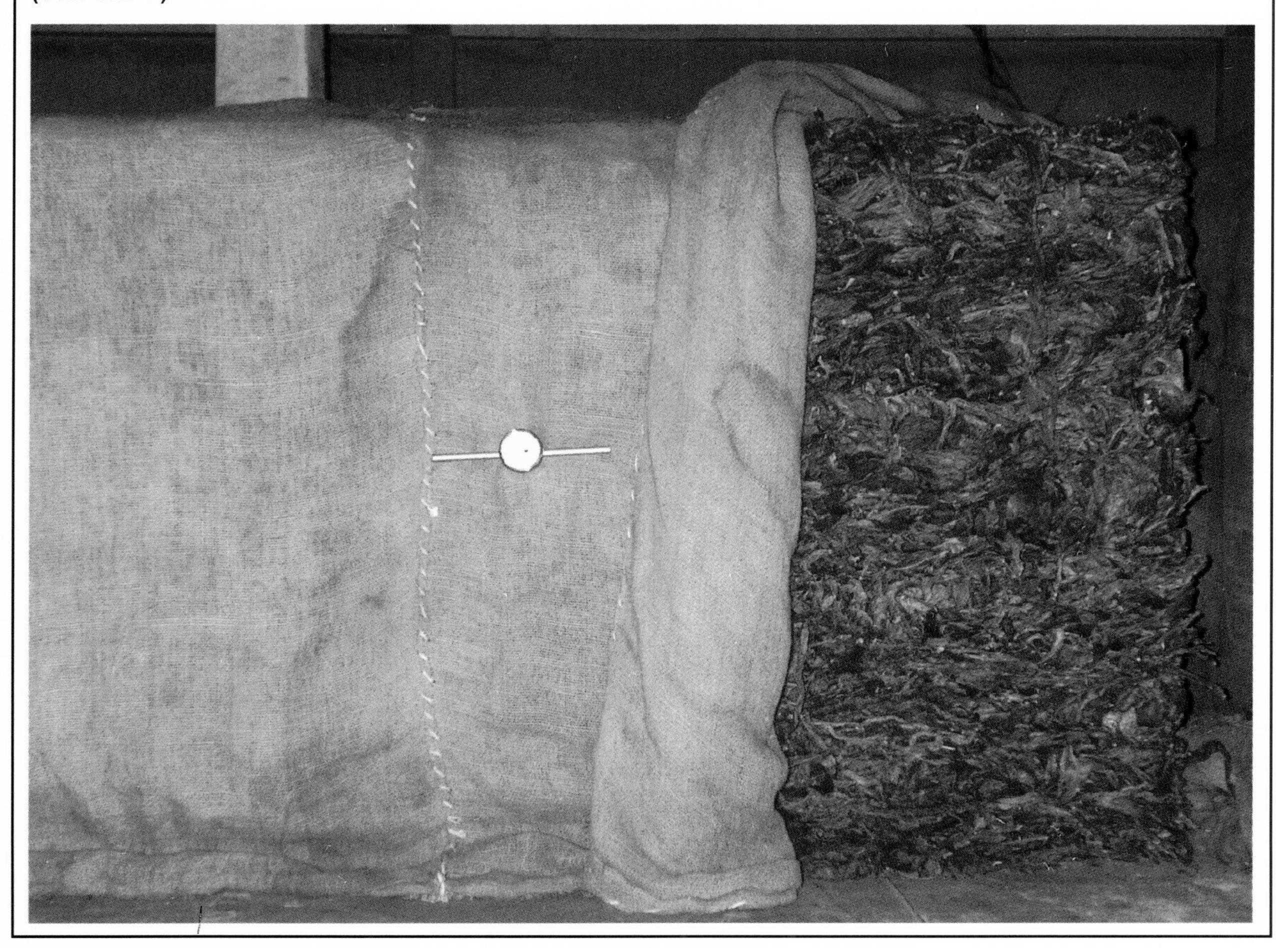

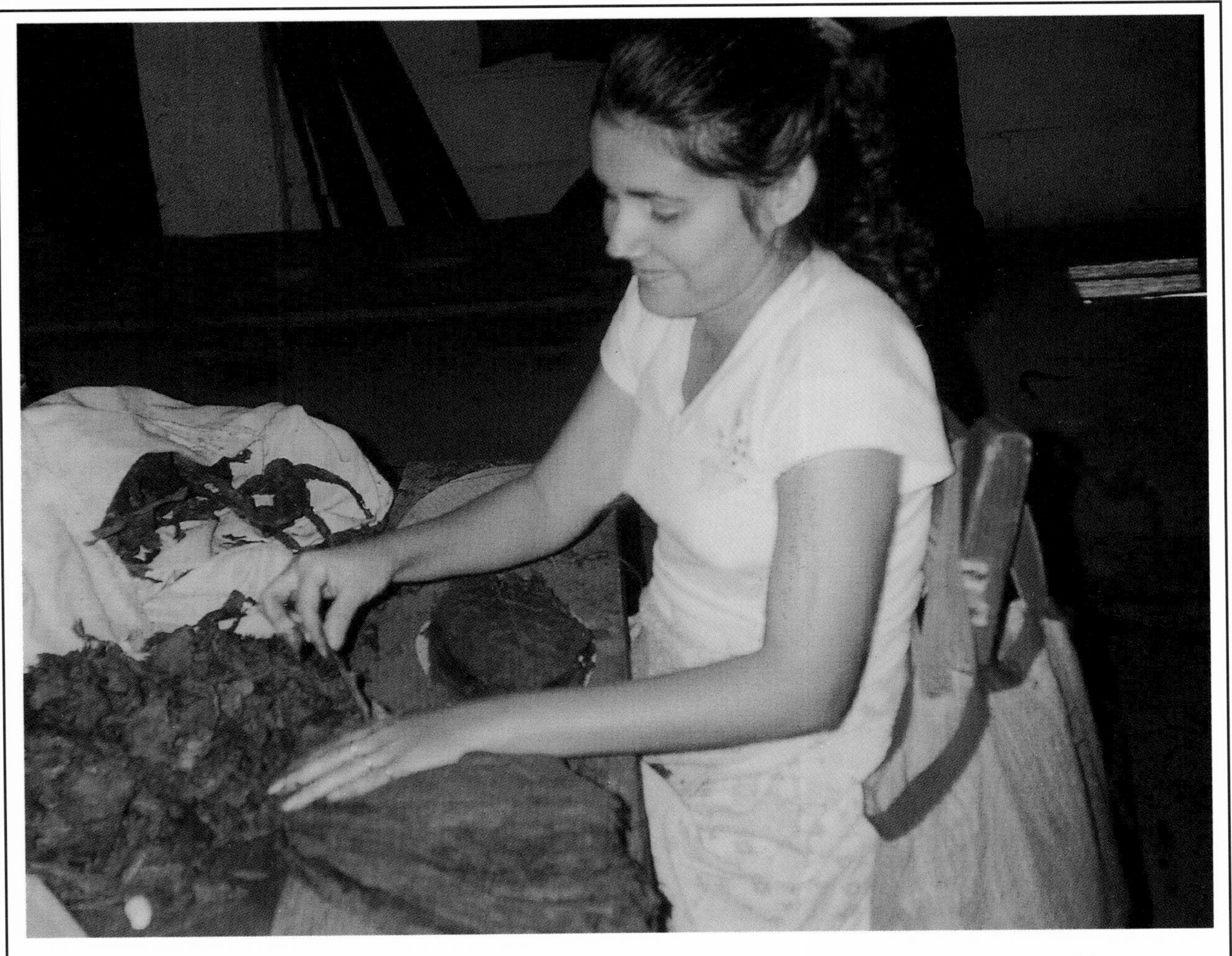

**After fermenting the tobacco is cleaned of any foreign matter or insects. This tobacco is not used for wrapper but may be used for binder and filler.**

on the class, stored for six months to one year undergoing a slow process of natural fermentation and aging. At the right time, this tobacco is taken to specialized stripping workshops where a new and intensive fermentation stage begins. Before stacking the piles, water is sprinkled on the tobacco leaves to reach a humidity of 25 to 30 per cent.That content of water starts a violent fermentation process that occasionaly generates temperatures above 50 degrees Centigrade; the piles must be closely watched to prevent overheating, which would ruin the tobacco. There are temperature tolerance and fermentation time norms for each tobacco category which depend directly on the desired physical and organoleptic qualities of the leaves.

When the last fermentation stage is finished, the stripping process begins. To make them fit for industrial use, each leaf has the thickest portion of its central nerve (about half of the total) eliminated manually. After stripping, the leaves are aired to eliminate all excess water, packed into bales and stored again until they are sent to the factories as raw material for the prized Cuban rolled cigars.

Tobacco coming from the choice open sunshine plantations - both sewn and on staff - is fermented in very much the same way as the one that comes from the prime plantations, but its classification is less complex. This kind of tobacco is generally exported as leaf-tobacco to be blended with other raw materials and improve their quality, or used domestically in the cigar and cigarette industries.

# CIGAR MANUFACTURE

The industrial process begins with the moistening of the tobacco leaves selected as wrapper, to soften and make them supple enough to be handled without getting torn or damaged. Next comes the stripping, which in the case of wrapper leaves the central nerve is completely eliminated, producing two halves or "sides" of leaf. The "sides" are then classified according to their color and size; the lighter ones are used for the smaller cigar types or "vitolas", while the darker ones are destined to the larger sizes.

While this is being done with the wrapper leaves, the binder and the blend of filler that will be used in a specific vitola are prepared at

**The capa is hung to dry and stabilize after it has been dampened.**

**The *Casa de Partagas* is just one of the many factories producing Havana cigars. This 1996 photo shows the factory as it now exists. It is visited daily by hundreds of foreign aficionados who buy their favorite cigars at about 30% of the price in their own country.**

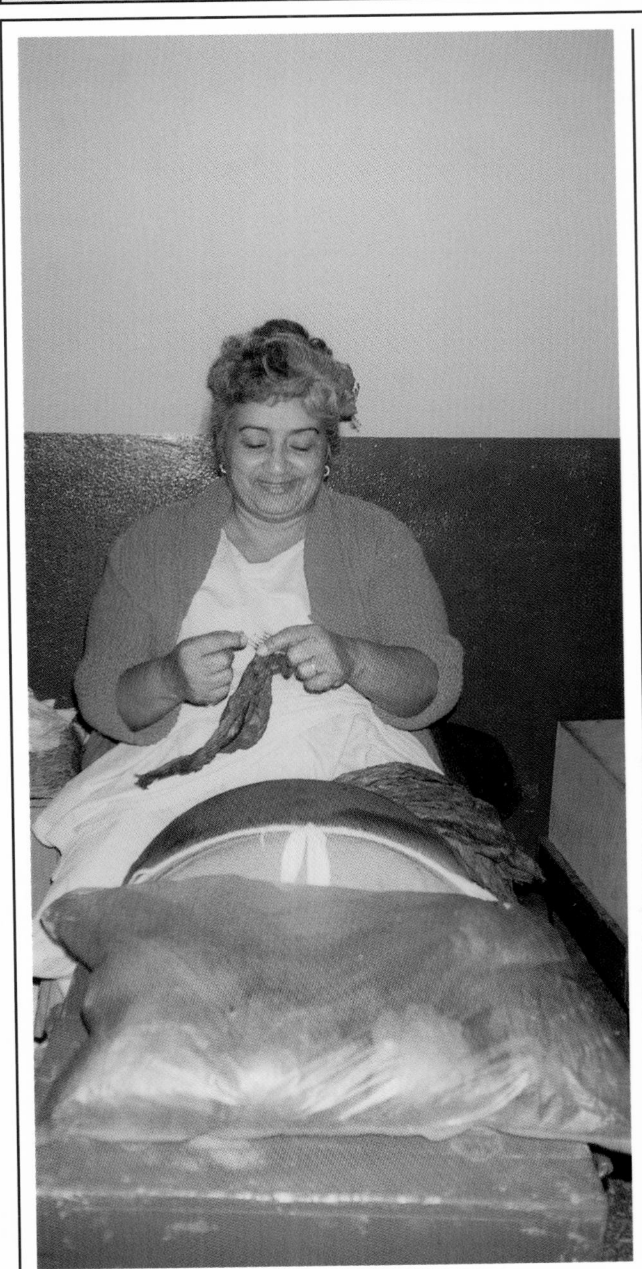

The *despalillo* is the removal of the central vein in the leaf thus dividing the leaf into two parts.

The dried leaves are anything but pliable and they must be remoistened or dampened before they are *worked*. The dampening makes them flexible and less likely to tear.

This lady in Havana is classifying the capa (wrapper) by size, color and quality. The longer the leaf, the larger the cigar size for which it can be used.

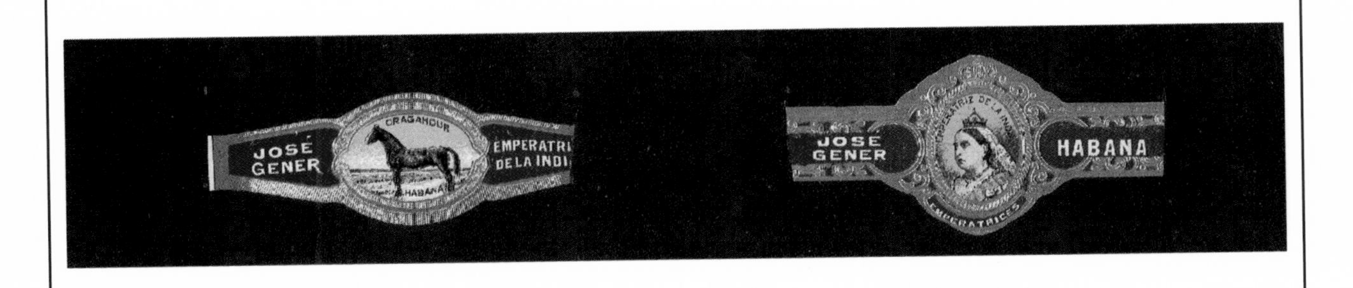

**Upper left:** Wrapper being rolled around a cigar in Havana.

**Center left:** Preparation of the filler and binder for various sizes and shapes of Habanos cigars.

**Bottom left:** Under a special light, an expert separates the finished cigars by their color so that each box will contain cigars of the same shade wrapper.

**Above:** The products are *aged* a bit and their humidity is stabilized in these wooden cabinets called *escaparates*.

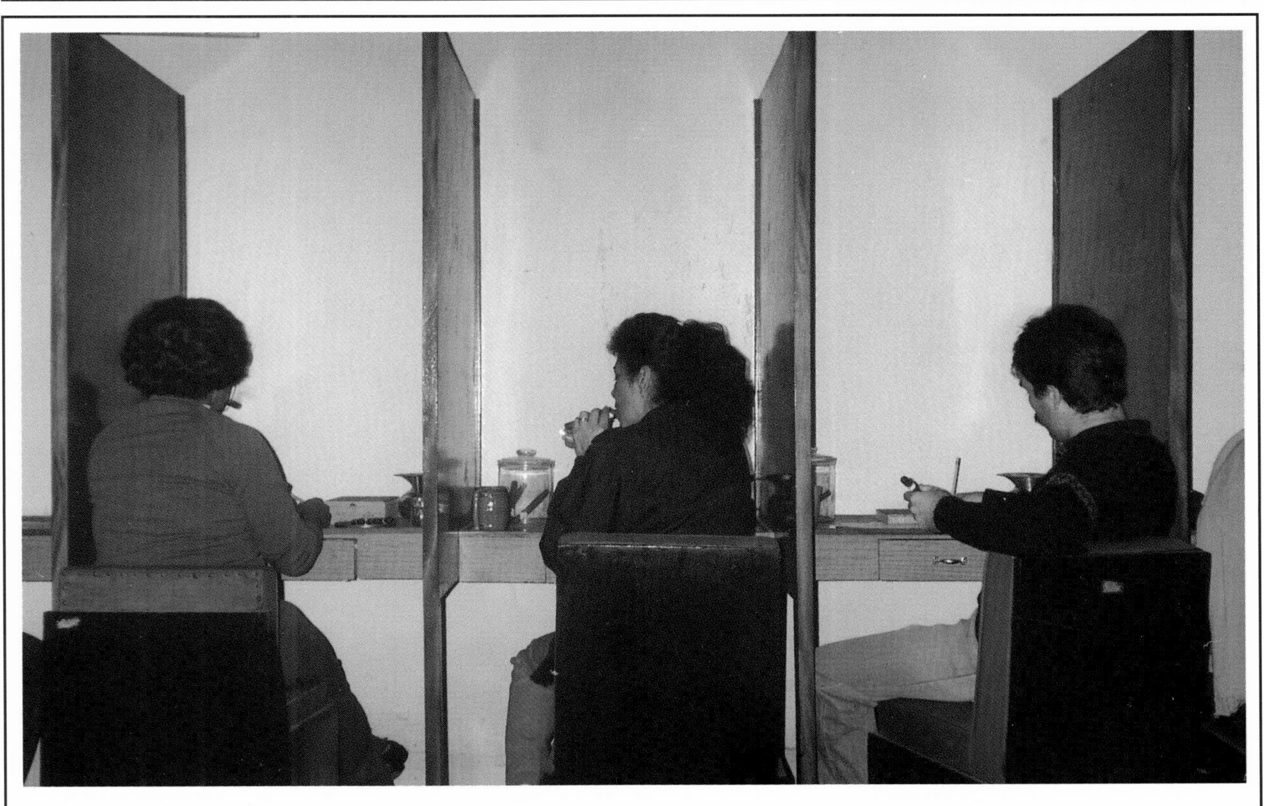

Above: The final, organoleptic (taste and smell) tests are made by individual tasters working in isolated booths. These tests guarantee the quality of Cuban *puros*.

Below: The boxes for most Habanos cigars are made by hand with each of the many decorations being added in the same factory in which the cigars are rolled.

the conditioning department. It is interesting to notice that binder leaves are always chosen from the "volado" category and that the basis for their selection is size. The choice of filler is a bit more complex because aside from size, it is necessary to know what kind of vitola will be made to guarantee that the right proportion of each kind of leaf is included in the blend. For instance, the filler for very small vitolas is generally made with No.1 Strength or "volado" leaves only. Medium sized vitolas require a blend of "volado" and "seco" leaves in fixed proportions that identify each vitola's aroma, taste and strength. Large vitolas normally carry blends of "volado", "seco" and "ligero" leaves. The No 4 Strength or "medio tiempo" leaves are only used in especially strong vitolas, which are uncommon in the Cuban cigar production.

Thus, in the factory galley each cigar roller receives the right amount of each kind of leaves required to make a fixed number of cigars of a given vitola. This guarantees production quality and uniformity with the best possible use of raw material. The finished cigars or "puros" are lightly sprayed against insect attack and then stored in wooden lockers called "escaparates", where they are kept for 48 to 72 hours until their humidity is completely stabilized.

**The final process is putting the cigars carefully into the boxes and being sure they are of uniform size.**

From the lockers, the cigars are taken to the color sorting room where they are expertly grouped to ensure that every layer in the boxes shows a perfectly even hue. Before the final packaging, each cigar is banded with a paper ring that identifies the brand. These bands are designed in countless forms and are generally very atractive. The bands and the beautiful prints that embellish the boxes make Havana cigars a highly refined product.

Finally, as part of the quality control procedures in every factory, a panel of tasters checks the organoleptic characteristics of the product by smoking samples of each batch of cigars. The Tasting Committee has a specially designed room where each taster can individually smoke and determine the quality of the product without any influence from his fellow tasters nor any prior information about the samples being evaluated, since these are always blind tests.

The judgement passed by the Tasting Committee on the finished cigars constitutes one of the determining factors for the approval of their commercialization as superior quality products. These rigorous tests and the strict technical control applied from the agricultural phase of tobacco up to its final stage in the industry help preserve the unaltered quality that distinguishes Habanos cigars throughout the world.

# BIBLIOGRAPHY

– Espino, E. *El mejoramiento del tabaco* (N. tabacum) *en Cuba.* Boletin de Reseña Tabaco No. 14.

– Espino, E.; Xiomara Rey; V. Garcia y H. Garcia. *'Habana P.R.': nueva variedad de tabaco negro* (N. tabacum L.) *con resistencia mútiple y buenas características comerciales.* Agrotecnia de Cuba 21 (2): 9-13, 1989.

– Espino, E.; Nilda Peñalver y Xiomara Rey. *Comportamiento inusual de la variedad 'Corojo' ante el ataque de la pata prieta* (Phytophthora parasitica var. nicotianae). *Cubataco Cienc. Téc.* –(La Habana) 3 (3): –, 1993 (En imprenta).

– Espino E.; Xiomara Rey y V. Garcia. *Obtención de lineas promisorias de tabaco negro. Perspectivas de algunas de ellas como futura variedades productoras de "capa".* Cultivos Agroindustriales. –(La Habana) 3 (3): – 1993 (En imprenta).

– Fernández de Madrid, José. *Memorias sobre el comercio, cultivo y elaboración del tabaco en esta siempre fiel Isla de Cuba.* La Habana, 1821. – 44 p.

– Gerstel, D. U. *Segregation in new allopolyploid of* Nicotiana. Genetics 45: 1723-1724, 1960.

– González del Valle, Angel. MEMORANDUM presentado a la Comisión Nacional de Propaganda y Defensa del Tabaco Habano. *La Habana,* noviembre 29 de 1928, – 410 p.

– Goodspeed, T.H. *The genus* Nicotiana. – Estados Unidos: Crónica Botábuca Co., 1954.

– Hasselbring, H. Tipes of cuban tobacco. *Bot. Gaz.* 53: 113-126, 1912.

– Lucas, G.B. *Diseases of tobacco.* –New York, The Scarecrow Press, 1975. –778 p.

– Mangeldorf, P. and Smith, C.E. *New archeological evidence on evolution of maize,* Bot. Mus. Seaf. Harvard University 13: 213-247. 1969.

– Ortiz, Fernándo. *Contrapunteo cubano del tabaco y el azúcar.* La Habana, Consejo Nacional de Cultura, 1963. –540 p.

– Reynoso, Alvaro. *Apuntes acerca de varios cultivos cubanos.* La Habana, 1867.

– Rodríguez Ferrer, Miguel. *El Tabaco Habano, su historia, su cultivo, sus vicisitudes y sus máa afamadas vegas en Cuba.* Madrid, 1851.

– Rodríguez Ramos, Manuel. *Siembra, fabricación e historia del tabaco.* La Habana, 1905.

– Salazar, Tomás. *Cartilla agraria para el cultivo del tabaco.* La Babana, 1850.

– Sarichev, Y.; Ivanitski, K. y Espino, E. *Filogénesis* de Nicotiana tabacum L. Información Directa Agrícola No. 10. 1976.

– Vavilov, N.I. *Studies on the origin of cultivated plants.* Leningrado Inst. Appl. Bot. Pl. Breed., 1926.